"Gerald Draws His Teacher" is based on a true story about Jerry Winick, the book's illustrator, when he was in the third grade at PS 128 in Brooklyn, New York.

This book is dedicated to all of our young students and aspiring artists everywhere.

Gerald is a boy who loves to draw.

He draws pictures
in his room.

Gerald likes to draw the things he sees around him. He hangs his drawings in his room.

One day Gerald asked his mom and dad if he could draw them.

They said "of course" and he drew them.

When he was done, Gerald's parents were so proud of the drawing, they hung it on the wall.

The next day, Gerald took his pad and pencils to school so he could draw his teacher, Mrs. Bradley.

During class, Gerald didn't pay attention to his teacher, he drew a picture of her instead.

When Mrs. Bradley saw Gerald drawing, she said "Gerald, bring the drawing to the front of the room".

Gerald walked nervously toward the front of the room with his drawing.

When Mrs. Bradley looked at the picture she was so surprised that the drawing looked just like her.

She said "You did a great drawing of me Gerald, but you must pay attention in class".

All of the kids in the class wanted to see Gerald's drawing.

When Gerald held up the picture, the kids cheered.

Gerald walked home from school that day, thinking about what had happened in class.

He knew he would always remember the day when Mrs. Bradley and his classmates loved his drawing. He also learned that he must pay attention in class.

CPSIA information can be obtained
at www.ICGtesting.com
Printed in the USA
LVRC092246220122
709137LV00003B/150